Excellence in Problem Solving Mathematics

Hilary Koll and Steve Mills

RISING STARS

Rising Stars UK Ltd.
7 Hatchers Mews, Bermondsey Street, London, SE1 3GS
www.risingstars-uk.com

Published 2010
Reprinted 2011

Authors: Hilary Koll and Steve Mills
Design and typesetting: Sally Boothroyd
Editorial: Bruce Nicholson, Ruth Burns
Artwork: Sally Boothroyd, Michael Emmerson, David Woodroffe
Cover Design: Words and Pictures

Photo acknowledgements
p.13 *tennis balls* © Timothy Large/iStockphoto; **p.16** *bowl of fruit* © Robyn Mackenzie/iStockphoto; **p.31** *nutritional info* © K Ledge/iStockphoto; **p.37** *gym* © Diego Cervo /iStockphoto; **p.38** *triangle artwork* © Qweek/iStockphoto; **p.39** *Pythagoras* © Hulton Archive/iStockphoto

British Library Cataloguing in Publication Data.
A CIP record for this book is available from the British Library.

ISBN: 978-1-84680-764-0

Printed by Craft Print International Ltd, Singapore.

Contents

Coverage of learning objectives of the Primary Framework for Mathematics Year 6

	Using and applying mathematics	Solve multi-step problems, and problems involving fractions, decimals and percentages; choose and use appropriate calculation strategies at each stage, including calculator use	Tabulate systematically the information in a problem or puzzle; identify and record the steps or calculations needed to solve it, using symbols where appropriate; interpret solutions in the original context and check their accuracy	Suggest, plan and develop lines of enquiry; collect, organise and represent information, interpret results and review methods; identify and answer related questions	Represent and interpret sequences, patterns and relationships involving numbers and shapes; suggest and test hypotheses; construct and use simple expressions and formulae in words then symbols, e.g. the cost of *c* pens at 15 pence each is 15c pence	Explain reasoning and conclusions, using words, symbols or diagrams as appropriate	Counting and understanding number	Find the difference between a positive and a negative integer, or two negative integers, in context	Use decimal notation for tenths, hundredths and thousandths; partition, round and order decimals with up to three places, and position them on the number line	Express a larger whole number as a fraction of a smaller one, e.g. recognise that 8 slices of a 5-slice pizza represents $\frac{8}{5}$ or $1\frac{3}{5}$ pizzas; simplify fractions by cancelling common factors; order a set of fractions by converting them to fractions with a common denominator	Express one quantity as a percentage of another, e.g. express £400 as a percentage of £1000; find equivalent percentages, decimals and fractions	Solve simple problems involving direct proportion by scaling quantities up or down	Knowing and using number facts	Use knowledge of place value and multiplication facts to 10 × 10 to derive related multiplication and division facts involving decimals, e.g. 0.8 × 7, 4.8 ÷ 6	Use knowledge of multiplication facts to derive quickly squares of numbers to 12×12 and the corresponding squares of multiples of 10	Recognise that prime numbers have only two factors and identify prime numbers less than 100; find the prime factors of two-digit numbers	Use approximations, inverse operations and tests of divisibility to estimate and check results
Sequences		✔	✔		✔	✔			✔					✔			
Mixed calculations (1)		✔	✔			✔								✔	✔		
Mixed calculations (2)		✔	✔			✔								✔	✔		
Fractions		✔	✔			✔				✔	✔						
Decimals		✔	✔			✔			✔		✔			✔			
Percentages		✔	✔			✔					✔						
Ratio and proportion		✔	✔			✔						✔					
Simple formulae		✔	✔		✔	✔											
Money and currencies		✔	✔			✔			✔					✔			
Negative numbers		✔	✔		✔	✔		✔									
Measures		✔	✔	✔		✔											
Area and perimeter		✔	✔			✔											
Reading scales		✔	✔			✔											
Time		✔	✔			✔											
Angles		✔	✔			✔											
Data handling		✔	✔	✔		✔											
Averages		✔	✔	✔		✔											
Probability		✔	✔	✔		✔											

																		Calculating
	✔					✔	✔		✔	✔	✔	✔	✔		✔	✔	✔	Calculate mentally with integers and decimals: U.t ± U.t, TU × U, TU ÷ U, U.t × U, U.t ÷ U
									✔	✔	✔	✔	✔		✔	✔	✔	Use efficient written methods to add and subtract integers and decimals, to multiply and divide integers and decimals by a one-digit integer, and to multiply two- and three-digit integers by a two-digit integer
												✔	✔	✔				Relate fractions to multiplication and division, e.g. $6 \div 5 = \frac{1}{5}$ of $6 = 6 \times \frac{1}{5}$; express a quotient as a fraction or decimal, e.g. $67 \div 5 = 13.4$ or $13\frac{2}{5}$; find fractions and percentages of whole-number quantities, e.g. $\frac{5}{8}$ of 96, 65% of £260
							✔					✔			✔	✔		Use a calculator to solve problems involving multi-step calculations
																		Understanding shape
						✔												Describe, identify and visualise parallel and perpendicular edges or faces and use these properties to classify 2-D shapes and 3-D solids
																		Make and draw shapes with increasing accuracy and apply knowledge of their properties
			✔															Visualise and draw on grids of different types where a shape will be after reflection, after translation, or after rotation through 90° or 180° about its centre or one of its vertices
																		Use coordinates in the first quadrant to draw, locate and complete shapes that meet given properties
			✔															Estimate angles, and use a protractor to measure and draw them, on their own and in shapes; calculate angles in a triangle or around a point
																		Measuring
				✔		✔	✔						✔					Select and use standard metric units of measure and convert between units using decimals to two places, e.g. change 2.75 litres to 2750 ml, or vice versa
					✔													Read and interpret scales on a range of measuring instruments, recognising that the measurement made is approximate and recording results to a required degree of accuracy; compare readings on different scales, e.g. when using different instruments
						✔												Calculate the perimeter and area of rectilinear shapes; estimate the area of an irregular shape by counting squares
																		Handling data
✔																		Describe and predict outcomes from data using the language of chance or likelihood
✔	✔	✔																Solve problems by collecting, selecting, processing, presenting and interpreting data, using ICT where appropriate; draw conclusions and identify further questions to ask
		✔																Construct and interpret frequency tables, bar charts with grouped discrete data, and line graphs; interpret pie charts
	✔																	Describe and interpret results and solutions to problems using the mode, range, median and mean

How to use this book

This book is designed to help you use your mathematical skills to solve a range of problems, many of which are written in words rather than figures.

Rather than giving a calculation like:

$4 \times 6 = \square$

a word problem might be something like:

If I have 4 six-packs of cola, how many cans of cola do I have in total?

The answer is the same, but you need to think about it a bit more and remember to answer by writing or saying: *I have 24 cans of cola in total.*

The example problem

The flow chart takes you through an example problem step-by-step. This is important when answering word problems as it helps you to order your thoughts, do each part of the problem in the right order and check your work!

Every problem has the same five steps:

READ the question, then read it again

DECIDE your operations and units

APPROXIMATE your answer

CALCULATE

CHECK your answer

We can remember this by using this mnemonic:

Rain
Drops
Are
Crystal
Clear

The introduction

This section of each page gives you an idea of the sort of problems you are likely to see and helps you to understand what maths you need to use.

PROBLEM SOLVING YEAR 6

Ratio and proportion

Ratio is the relationship between two or more quantities, e.g. the amount of blackcurrant to water in a juice drink or the numbers of boys and girls in a class.

This recipe is for 16 courgette patties.

If Alice wants to make 12 courgette patties, how much flour should she use?

Courgette patties
240 g courgettes
160 g onions
80 g feta cheese
200 g potatoes
120 g flour
100 g breadcrumbs
Egg to bind

Read the question, now read it again. — Read slowly. Write the information clearly, for example:

patties	:	flour
16	:	120 g
12	:	?

Decide your operations and units. — I need to find how much flour for 1 patty and then multiply by 12.

Approximate your answer. — The answer will be about $\frac{3}{4}$ of 120 g, which is 90 g.

Calculate. — I divide 120 g by 16 to get the amoun[t] of flour for 1 patty = 7.5 g; 7.5 g × 12 = 90 g

Check. — I can check by re-reading the questio[n] to make sure my answer makes sens[e]

Hints and tips When working out ratios, remember to multiply or divide both numbers in a ratio by the same number to get an equivalent ratio.

÷16	16	:	120 g
×12	1	:	7.5 g
	12	:	90 g

22

Hints and tips

The Hints and tips section gives you useful ideas for completing the problems on the opposite page. These are the things you need to remember if you are doing a quiz or test.

RATIO AND PROPORTION

Questions

1 a) Look at the recipe opposite. Emile wants to make 8 courgette patties. How many grams of onions will he need?

b) Mrs Jones wants to make 4 courgette patties. How many grams of potatoes should she use?

c) Alice wants to make 12 courgette patties. How much feta cheese will she need?

2 a) Alice wants to make 12 courgette patties. How many grams of courgettes and how many grams of breadcrumbs will she need?

b) Emile wants to make 6 courgette patties. How much flour should he use?

c) Lucy changes all the amounts in the recipe so that she can make 24 courgette patties. How many grams of courgettes and how many grams of onions will she need?

CHALLENGE

Luke changes all the amounts in the recipe so he can make 24 courgette patties. He mixes all the ingredients (except the eggs) together. What is the total mass of the mixture?

Explore

Choose your favourite recipe. Does it say how many people the recipe is for, or how many cakes it makes, etc.? Change all the amounts in the recipe so that it makes a different amount, but all the ingredients stay in the same ratio.

23

The questions

The questions get harder as you go down the page.

- Section 1 questions are fairly straightforward and help you to practise your skills.
- Section 2 questions are a bit harder. They will help you to remember all the key points.

Challenge

The Challenge is really tough and sometimes involves making up games and your own questions.

Explore

This section gives you a chance to investigate the topic in more depth and to make links with other subjects. You may be asked to write about something or do some research.

Ten top tips for working with word problems

1 *Work step-by-step.* Follow the flow chart.

Rain	**Read** the question, now read it again.
Drops	**Decide** your operations and units.
Are	**Approximate** your answer.
Crystal	**Calculate.**
Clear	**Check.**

2 Always *show your working* or ‘method’. This will help you to keep track of what you have done and may help you to get extra marks.

3 Always *include the units* in your answer. If you don’t, you won’t get full marks.

4 When you first read through a question, *underline important words and numbers*. This will help you to remember the important bits.

5 *Draw a picture to help you.* Sometimes a question is easier if you can 'see' it. For example, drawing 6 apples can help you if you need to divide them.

6 If the problem has a number of steps, break it down and do *one step at a time*.

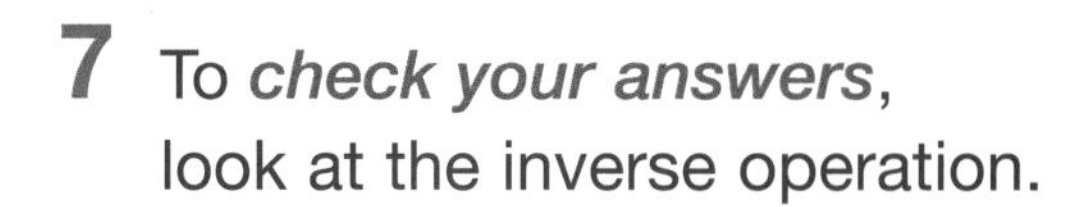

7 To *check your answers*, look at the inverse operation.

8 Sometimes an answer will 'sound right'. Read it out (quietly) and listen. *Does it make sense?*

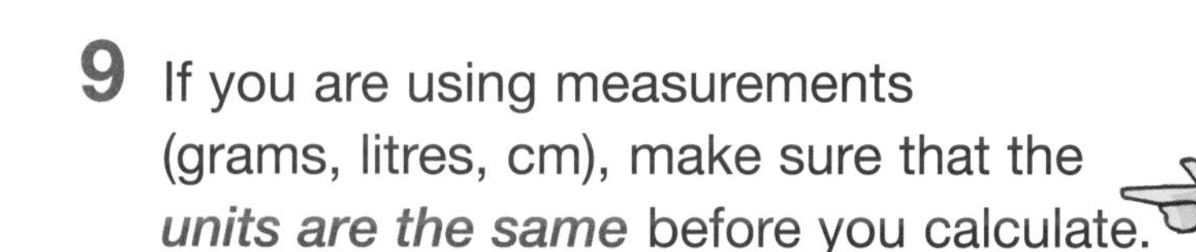

9 If you are using measurements (grams, litres, cm), make sure that the *units are the same* before you calculate.

10 Once again! *Read the question again and check that your solution answers it.*

Sequences

Some sequences go up or down in equal-sized steps, but others may follow a multiplying rule, or go up or down in non-equal steps.

This sequence has the rule:

To get each new term, add 1 to the previous number, then multiply by 3.

Which two numbers are under the flaps?

Read the question, now read it again.

Read slowly and carefully. What are you being asked to do?

Decide your operations and units.

I need to add 1 to 30 and multiply by 3 and then repeat by adding 1 and multiplying by 3 to get the next number.

Approximate your answer.

The first number is about $3 \times 30 = 90$ and the second number is about $3 \times 90 = 270$.

Calculate.

$30 + 1 = 31$; $31 \times 3 = 93$;
$93 + 1 = 94$; $94 \times 3 = 282$
The numbers under the flaps are 94 and 282.

Check.

I can add 1 to 282 and multiply by 3 to see if I reach 849. Yes, I do!

Hints and tips

Always check your answers by continuing the sequence until you reach a given number, or by counting back.

Questions

1

Which numbers are under the flaps?

a) The rule is: *multiply the previous number by 2 and then add 5.*

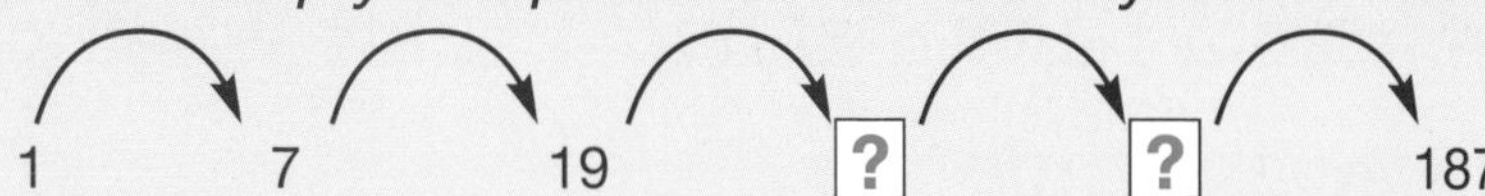

b) The rule is: *subtract 5 from the previous number and then divide by 10.*

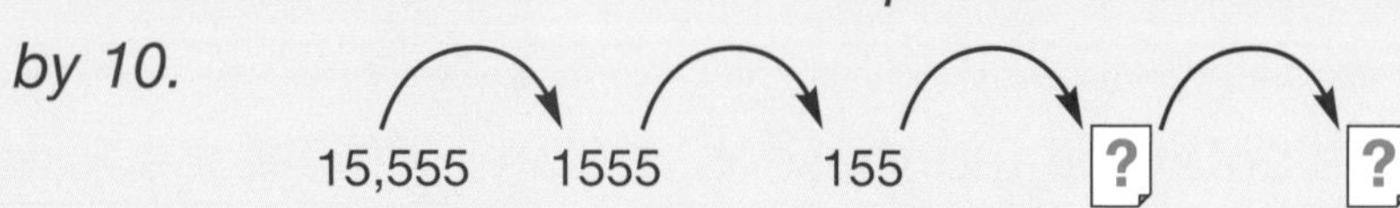

c) The rule is: *halve the previous number and then add 12.*

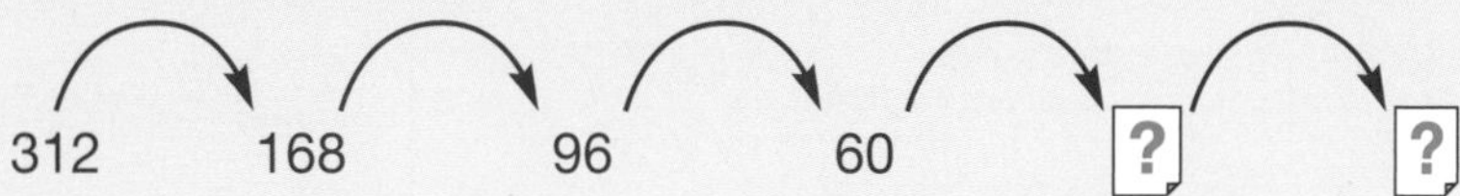

2

Find the missing numbers in these sequences.

a) The rule is: *multiply the previous number by 2 and then add 0.4.*

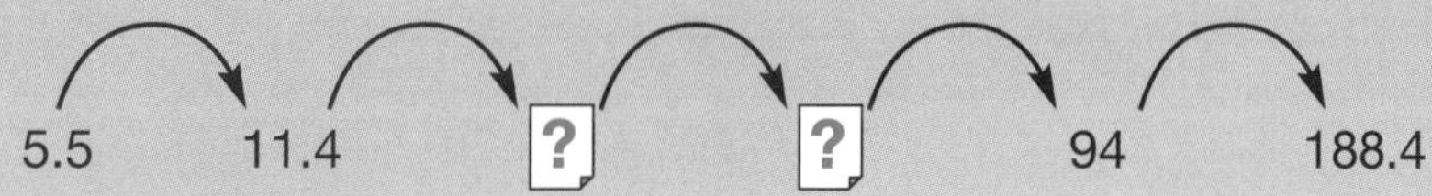

b) The rule is: *add 10 to the previous number and then divide by 2.*

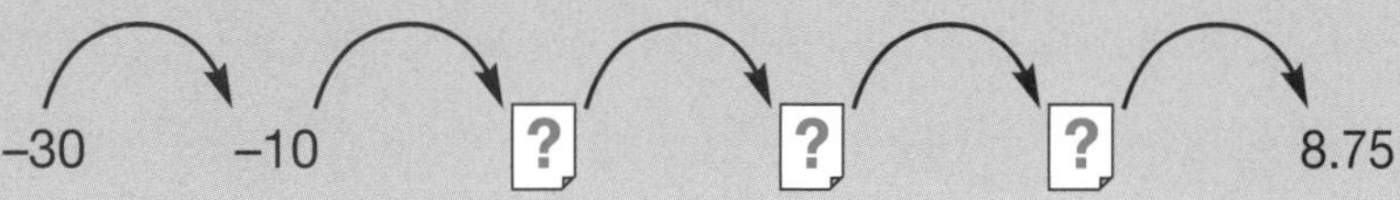

CHALLENGE

Make up three of your own number sequences using a rule like the ones above. List the first six numbers in each sequence.

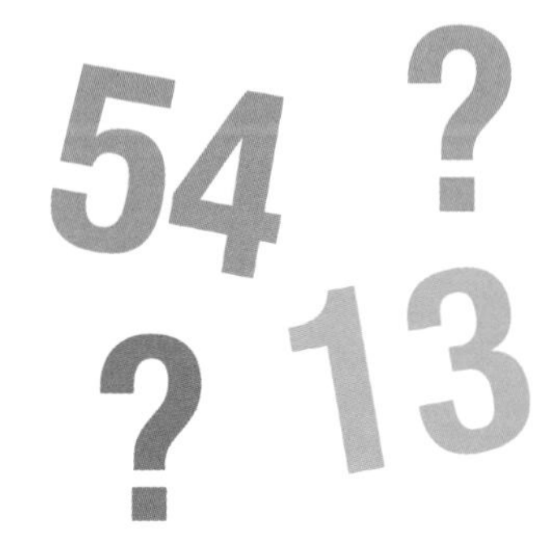

Explore

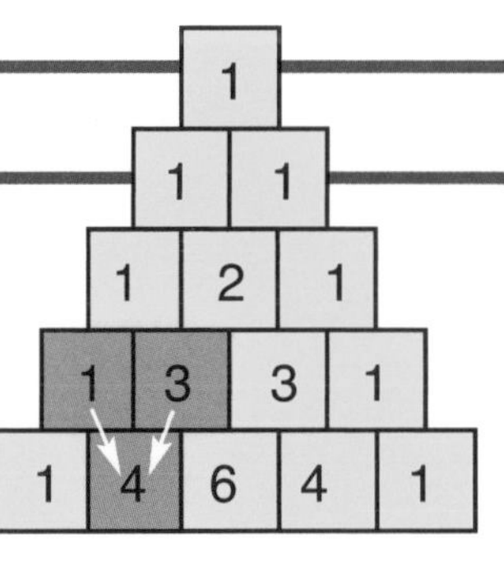

Look in books or on the Internet to find out about a special sequence called 'Pascal's triangle'. There are many patterns in the rows of numbers. Make a poster about the patterns you find.

Go to **www.mathsisfun.com/pascals-triangle.html** for more information.

Mixed calculations (1)

For some word problems you need to select the correct pieces of information from a table and then decide whether to add, subtract, multiply or divide.

This table shows the diameters and masses of some different sports balls.

Ball	Diameter (cm)	Mass (g)
Football	22.8	464.1
Snooker ball	5.25	120.5
Table tennis ball	3.8	2.68
Tennis ball	6.35	58.9
Hockey ball	7.32	158
Cricket ball	7.13	155.9
Squash ball	4.04	24.7
Volleyball ball	21.4	271.7

How much lighter is the table tennis ball than the snooker ball?

Read the question, now read it again.

Read slowly and carefully.
What is the important information?

Decide your operations and units.

I need to find the difference between 2.68 g and 120.50 g, by subtracting 2.68 from 120.50.

Approximate your answer.

121 g – 3 g = 118 g

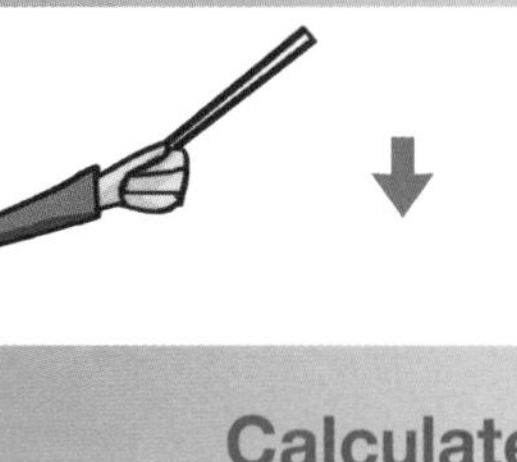

I'll use a written method and put a zero on 120.50, so that both numbers have 2 digits after the decimal point.

Calculate.

```
 1 9 14 1
120.50
 –2.68
------
117.82
```

The answer is 117.82 g.

Check.

I'll add 117.82 and 2.68 to make sure it is 120.50. I'm right!

Hints and tips

The diameter is the width of the ball at its widest point. When adding or subtracting decimals it is often easier to add zeroes so that both decimals have the same number of decimal places. For example, write 6.7 – 4.36 as 6.70 – 4.36.

Questions

1

a) Look at the table opposite. How much larger is the diameter of the cricket ball than the diameter of the squash ball?

b) How much lighter is the tennis ball than the cricket ball?

c) How much larger is the diameter of the football than the diameter of the volleyball ball?

2

a) Which ball is exactly 6 times wider than the table tennis ball?

b) The mass of which ball mass is exactly 11 times that of the squash ball?

c) Which two balls have masses with a difference of 2.1 g?

CHALLENGE

Mr Penn picks up all the tennis balls and puts them in a bag. The balls and the bag together weigh 1.4 kg. What is the mass of the bag?

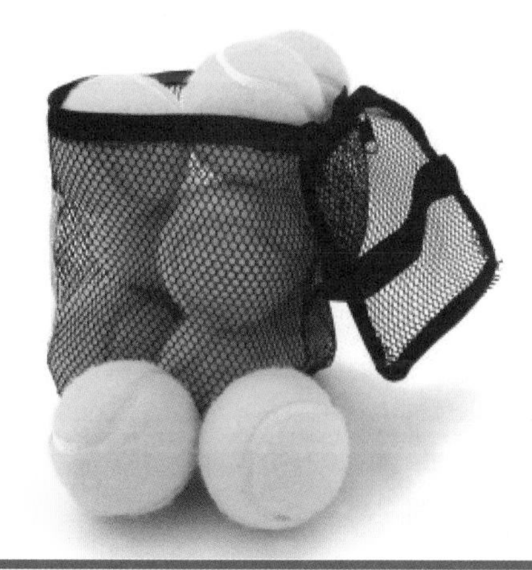

Explore

Use some string to measure the **circumference** of a ball (the distance all around it at its widest point). The circumference of a ball or circle is always just over three times larger than its diameter. This number, just over three, is the special number, **pi** (π). Look online to find out more about it.

Mixed calculations (2)

It is important to be able to work out whether to add, subtract, multiply or divide, or to do a combination of these, to find the answer to a word problem.

A school is having a sponsored sports day. Jamie is sponsored 50p for every 10 cm he jumps in the long jump. He jumps 4.2 m. How much money does he raise?

Read the question, now read it again.

Read slowly and carefully. Which are the important numbers?

Decide your operations and units.

I need to find how many lots of 10 cm are in 4.2 m (which is 420 cm) and then multiply the answer by 50p.

Approximate your answer.

There are 10 lots of 10 cm in each metre, so it'll be about 40 × 50p which is 2000p or £20.

Calculate.

420 cm ÷ 10 cm = 42;
42 × 50p = 2100p = £21.00

Check.

50p is half £1 and half of 42 is 21. Yes, I was correct!

Hints and tips

Remember to check the units of amounts or measurements so that the units are the same. For example, make sure you change centimetres to metres, or vice versa.

Questions

1 a) Philip is sponsored to run as many laps around the field as he can. He is sponsored 75p per lap. How many laps does he run if he raises £20.25?

b) Raheed is sponsored to run 20 laps around the field. He must run the 20 laps in in less than 18 minutes to raise the money. If his lap average time is 45 seconds, will he raise the money?

2 a) Lillie's task is to throw the bean bag. For every 10 cm over 3.5 metres she throws the bag, she is sponsored 37p. How much will she raise if she throws the bean bag 480 cm?

b) Jasmine is also throwing the bean bag. For every 5 cm over 4 metres she throws it, she is sponsored 65p. How much will she raise if she throws the bean bag 4.75 cm?

CHALLENGE

Which of these three children raises the most money?

- Harry gets £1.50 for every 20 cm further than 3 metres he jumps in the long jump. He jumps 420 cm.
- Janine gets 28p for every 5 laps she runs around the field. She runs 35 laps.
- Chloe throws the bean bag. For every 5 cm over 4 metres that she throws it, she is sponsored 75p. How much will she raise if she throws the bean bag 4.7 cm?

Explore

How far can you jump along the ground? Do the long jump and measure it. Can you jump further than your partner? Find out the world record for the long jump and compare your jump with this.

Fractions

For some fraction word problems it helps to convert the fractions so that they all have the same denominator. This makes them easier to work with.

There are apples, bananas and pears in a fruit bowl. $\frac{5}{8}$ of the pieces of fruit are apples, $\frac{1}{4}$ of them are bananas and two are pears. How many apples are there?

Read the question, now read it again.

The question doesn't tell me how many pieces of fruit there are.

Decide your operations and units.

I'll change all the fractions so that the denominators are 8 and find out what fraction of the pieces of fruit must be pears. Then, I'll use this to work out how many are in the bowl altogether.

Approximate your answer.

Calculate.

Apples $\frac{5}{8}$, bananas $\frac{1}{4} = \frac{2}{8}$, pears = ?

$\frac{5}{8} + \frac{2}{8} = \frac{7}{8}$, so the pears must be $\frac{1}{8}$. If two pears are $\frac{1}{8}$ there must be $2 \times 8 = 16$ pieces of fruit in the bowl. So $\frac{5}{8}$ of 16 = 10 apples.

Check.

I'll check each fruit to make sure the total is 16. Ten apples, four bananas, two pears = 16. Yes, I was correct!

Hints and tips

If changing a fraction to an equivalent one, always multiply or divide the **numerator** (the number on the top) and the **denominator** (the number on the bottom) by the same number.

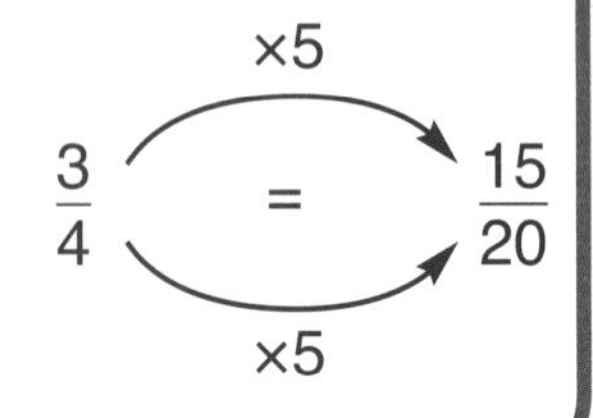

Questions

1

a) There are geese and ducks in a farmyard. If $\frac{1}{4}$ of the birds are geese and 9 are ducks, how many are geese?

b) There are men, women and children in a park. If $\frac{1}{5}$ of the people are men, $\frac{3}{7}$ are women and 13 are children, how many are men?

c) Saimma keeps fish in a tank. If $\frac{2}{3}$ are angelfish, $\frac{1}{5}$ are guppies and there are 4 catfish, how many angelfish are there?

2

a) Anna can see some amphibians in a pond. If $\frac{1}{6}$ are frogs, $\frac{2}{5}$ are newts and there are 26 toads, how many frogs are there?

b) Farmer Peters keeps animals in a field. If $\frac{1}{6}$ are cows, $\frac{1}{8}$ are horses, $\frac{5}{12}$ are sheep and there are 7 goats, how many sheep are there?

c) There are apples, bananas, pears and peaches in a fruit bowl. In the bowl, $\frac{3}{8}$ of the pieces of fruit are apples, $\frac{1}{4}$ of them are bananas, $\frac{1}{16}$ of them are pears and there are 5 peaches. How many bananas are there?

CHALLENGE

Write some fraction puzzles of your own for a partner to answer. Don't forget to work out the answers!

Explore

Did you know that the Ancient Egyptians used fractions? They only used fractions with the numerator (top number) 1, such as $\frac{1}{4}$, $\frac{1}{7}$, $\frac{1}{8}$ and so on. Fractions such as $\frac{3}{4}$ would be written as $\frac{1}{2} + \frac{1}{4}$ or $\frac{5}{6}$ would be written as $\frac{1}{2} + \frac{1}{3}$. Can you work out how they would have written $\frac{7}{8}$ or $\frac{3}{5}$?

Decimals

When solving decimal word problems, it can help to treat the decimals like whole numbers. For example, 0.17 can be thought of as 17 divided by 100.

On the Moon, a person's weight is 0.17 times their weight on Earth. On the planet Mercury, a person's weight is twice that on the Moon. If a man weighs 75 kg on Earth, what is his weight on Mercury?

Read the question, now read it again.

Read carefully. Write the important numbers and their units.

Decide your operations and units.

I need to multiply 75 by 0.17.
I'll do this by multiplying 75 by 17 and then dividing by 100.
Finally, I need to double the answer.

Approximate your answer.

$75 \times 20 \div 100 = 1500 \div 100 = 15$;
$15 \times 2 = 30$
The answer will be about 30 kg.

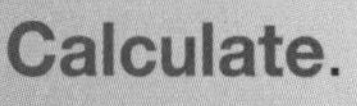

Calculate.

$75\,\text{kg} \times 0.17 = 12.75\,\text{kg}$;
$12.75\,\text{kg} \times 2 = 25.5\,\text{kg}$.

Check.

I can double 0.17 to make 0.34, multiply 75 by 0.34 to see if I get 25.5 kg. Yes, I do!

Hints and tips

Be careful to read the questions carefully to make sure you know whether the person's weight given is their weight on Earth, or their weight on another planet.

Questions

a) On the planet Neptune, a person's weight is 1.4 times their weight on Earth. If a woman weighs 60 kg on Earth, what is her weight on Neptune?

b) On the planet Mars, a person's weight is 0.38 times their weight on Earth. If a boy weighs 54 kg on Earth, what is his weight on Mars?

c) On the planet Uranus, a person's weight is 1.4 times their weight on Earth. If a girl weighs 50 kg on Earth, what is her weight on Uranus?

2

a) On the planet Venus, a person's weight is 0.9 times their weight on Earth. If a man weighs 63 kg on Venus, what is his weight on Earth?

b) On the planet Mars, a person's weight is 0.38 times their weight on Earth. On the planet Saturn, a person's weight is three times that on Mars. If a man weighs 80 kg on Earth, what is his weight on Saturn?

CHALLENGE

Go to **www.exploratorium.edu/ronh/weight/** to find your own weight on other planets. Write a fact sheet about what you have found out.

Explore

Find out about the sizes of the different planets and their distances from the Sun. Make a card for each planet, showing this and any other interesting information that you find out.

Percentages

Percent means 'out of a hundred'. Percentages are another way of showing fractions with the denominator 100, e.g. $\frac{4}{100}$ = 4% and $\frac{58}{100}$ = 58%.

At a snooker tournament £125 000 was given as prize money. 76% of the prize money was given to the winner and 18% to the runner-up. The rest was shared equally between the two other semi-finalists.

How much money was won by the each semi-finalist?

Read the question, now read it again.	Read slowly and carefully. What is the the question asking?
Decide your operations and units.	I'll add 76% and 18% and subtract the percentage from 100%. Then, I'll halve the answer and find that percentage of £125 000.
Approximate your answer.	The semi-finalists will each get about 3% of £125 000. I think that will be a bit more than £3000.
Calculate.	76 + 18 = 94; 100 − 94 = 6; 6% ÷ 2 = 3%. 1% of £125 000 is £1250 so 3% is £1250 × 3 = £3750.
Check.	I could work out all the amounts and check they add to £125 000. Yes, they do!

Hints and tips

When finding percentages of numbers and quantities, find 1% by dividing by 100 first and then multiply to find that percentage.

Questions

a) A snooker player wins £95 000 in a tournament. He gives 7% of the prize money to charity. How much does he give to charity?

b) At a snooker tournament 8% of the 550 frames played involved century breaks (where a player scored more than 100). How many century breaks were there?

c) For one tournament £250 000 is given as prize money. Of this, 80% is given to the winner and 10% to the runner-up. How much does the winner receive?

2

a) 8425 people come to watch a snooker tournament. 52% of them are men and the rest are women. How many are women?

b) Of the £250 000 given as prize money, 80% is given to the winner and 10% to the runner-up. The rest is shared equally between the two other semi-finalists. How much does each semi-finalist receive?

c) A snooker champion wins £250 000 in a tournament. He gives 10% of the prize money to charity, uses 15% to buy a car and gives the rest to his family. How much does he give to his family?

CHALLENGE

At a tournament £275 000 is given as prize money. Of this, 65% is given to the winner, 21% to second place, 5% to the two other semi-finalists and the rest is shared equally between the four other quarter-finalists. How much money does each quarter-finalist win?

Explore

Find out about how to score in snooker. What is the highest that can be scored in a single break? Write which balls must be potted to reach this score.

Ratio and proportion

Ratio is the relationship between two or more quantities, e.g. the amount of blackcurrant to water in a juice drink or the numbers of boys and girls in a class.

This recipe is for 16 courgette patties.

If Alice wants to make 12 courgette patties, how much flour should she use?

Courgette patties

240 g courgettes
160 g onions
80 g feta cheese
200 g potatoes
120 g flour
100 g breadcrumbs
Egg to bind

Read the question, now read it again.

Read slowly. Write the information clearly, for example:

patties	:	flour
16	:	120 g
12	:	?

Decide your operations and units.

I need to find how much flour for 1 patty and then multiply by 12.

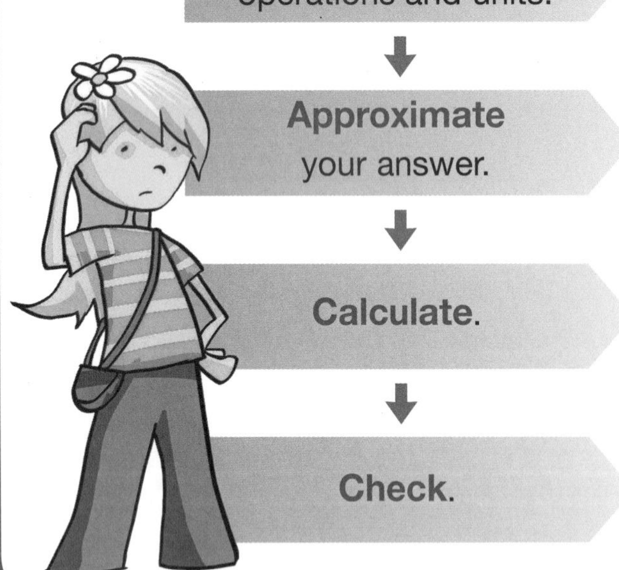

Approximate your answer.

The answer will be about $\frac{3}{4}$ of 120 g, which is 90 g.

Calculate.

I divide 120 g by 16 to get the amount of flour for 1 patty = 7.5 g;
7.5 g × 12 = 90 g

Check.

I can check by re-reading the question to make sure my answer makes sense!

Hints and tips

When working out ratios, remember to multiply or divide both numbers in a ratio by the same number to get an equivalent ratio.

÷16	16	:	120 g	÷16
	1	:	7.5 g	
×12	12	:	90 g	×12

Questions

1

a) Look at the recipe opposite. Emile wants to make 8 courgette patties. How many grams of onions will he need?

b) Mrs Jones wants to make 4 courgette patties. How many grams of potatoes should she use?

c) Alice wants to make 12 courgette patties. How much feta cheese will she need?

2

a) Alice wants to make 12 courgette patties. How many grams of courgettes and how many grams of breadcrumbs will she need?

b) Emile wants to make 6 courgette patties. How much flour should he use?

c) Lucy changes all the amounts in the recipe so that she can make 24 courgette patties. How many grams of courgettes and how many grams of onions will she need?

CHALLENGE!

Luke changes all the amounts in the recipe so he can make 24 courgette patties. He mixes all the ingredients (except the eggs) together. What is the total mass of the mixture?

Explore

Choose your favourite recipe. Does it say how many people the recipe is for, or how many cakes it makes, etc.? Change all the amounts in the recipe so that it makes a different amount, but all the ingredients stay in the same ratio.

Simple formulae

When solving some problems you might be asked to use a formula to help you work out the answer. Substitute the numbers given, by swapping them for the letters.

At a theme park, the overall cost (C) in pounds for the entrance fee is £3, plus £2 for each ride (r) that you go on. This can be written as the formula: $C = 3 + (2 \times r)$. David went on 6 rides. What was his total cost (C) in pounds?

Read the question, now read it again.

Read slowly and carefully and make a note of the numbers.

Decide your operations and units.

I must substitute 6 for r and then multiply by 2 and add 3 to get the overall cost (C).

Approximate your answer.

I think the cost will be about £15.

Calculate.

$C = 3 + (2 \times r)$, so $C = 3 + (2 \times 6) = 3 + 12 = 15$, so his cost is £15.

Check.

I will re-read the question and check the formula to make sure I understood it correctly.

Hints and tips

When a formula has brackets, remember to do the part in the brackets first.

Questions

a) Using the formula opposite, find the overall cost (C) in pounds if Randeep went on 10 rides.

b) Joel went on 8 rides. What is Joel's overall cost (C) in pounds?

c) At a different theme park, the overall cost (C) in pounds is £1 for the entrance fee, plus £3 for each ride (r) that you go on. This can be written as the formula $C = 1 + (3 \times r)$. Gita went on 7 rides. What was her overall cost (C) in pounds?

2

a) The formula for finding the area (A) of a rectangle is $A = l \times w$, where l is the length and w is the width. Use the formula to find the area (A) of a rectangle (in cm^2) with length (l) 8 cm and width (w) 6 cm.

b) The formula for finding the perimeter (P) of a rectangle is $P = 2 \times (l + w)$, where again l is the length and w is the width. Use the formula to find the perimeter (P) of a rectangle (in cm) with length (l) 13 cm and width (w) 6 cm.

c) The formula for (approximately) converting number of kilometres (k) into miles (s) is $s = k \times 5 \div 8$. Use this formula to convert 160 kilometres into miles.

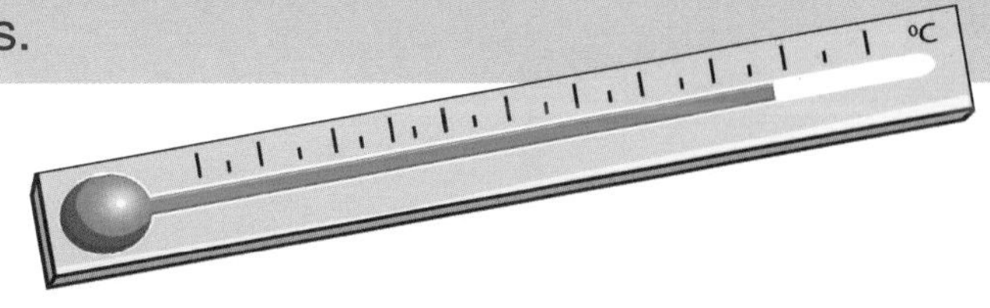

CHALLENGE

Find out the formula for converting temperatures given in degrees Fahrenheit into degrees Celsius. Look online at sites such as www.weatherquestions.com/How_do_you_convert_temperature.htm.

Explore

One of the most famous scientific formulas is $E = mc^2$. It was made famous by Albert Einstein. Do you know what he looked like? Find out about him and what he achieved. Write a leaflet explaining why he is famous, including as much information as you can.

Money and currencies

When a problem asks you to find prices in different currencies you must use the *exchange rate*. You can use a calculator for these problems.

In a magazine on a plane there are duty-free items and gifts for sale. They can be bought in British pounds (£) or in Euros (€). The exchange rate is £1 = €1.20. What is the price of this watch in pounds (£), if the Euro price is €25.20?

Read the question, now read it again.

Read slowly and carefully. Is the amounts given in pounds or Euros?

Decide your operations and units.

I have been given the Euro price, so I must divide it by the exchange rate (£1 = €1.20) and then make sure my answer is written correctly in pounds.

Approximate your answer.

For any amount, the number of Euros will always be more than the number of pounds, so the answer will be less than £25.20.

Calculate.

25.20 ÷ 1.20 = 21. This means £21.

Check.

I can multiply 21 by 1.20 (the exchange rate) to check it is 25.20. Yes, it is!

Hints and tips

To convert from pounds to another currency, *multiply* by the exchange rate.
To convert back to pounds, *divide* by the exchange rate.

Questions

Use the exchange rate £1 = €1.20 to answer these three questions.

a) Find the £ price of a bottle of perfume if the Euro price is €18.00.

b) The price of a mascara is £25. How much is this in Euros?

c) The price of a mobile phone is €174.60. How much is this in pounds?

a) The exchange rate for US dollars ($) is £1 = $1.51. How much is £5.45 in US dollars? Round your answer to the nearest cent.

b) The exchange rate for US dollars ($) is £1 = $1.51. How much is $35.70 in pounds? Round your answer to the nearest penny.

c) The exchange rate for Japanese yen is £1 = 133.50 yen. You can buy a watch for £44 or for 5300 yen. Which is cheaper and by how many pounds is it cheaper?

CHALLENGE!

The exchange rate for US dollars ($) is £1 = $1.51 and for Japanese yen it is £1 = 133.50 yen. You can buy a digital music player for £455, for $689 or for 60 000 yen. Which is the cheapest and by how many pounds is it cheaper than the other two?

Explore

Go to the currency converter at **www.xe.com** and find the exchange rates for other currencies. Be aware that exchange rates change regularly. Choose the price in pounds of something you would like to buy and make a poster to show its price in lots of other currencies.

Negative numbers

Negative numbers are those that are lower or less than zero. We use negative numbers for cold temperatures, e.g. –4°C, and for numbers below ground or below sea level.

A bungee jumper bounces up and down on a bungee rope. Where does he end up?

- He starts at 12 m.
- He goes down 28 m.
- Then up 24 m.
- Then down 13 m.
- Then up 7 m.
- Then down 6 m.
- And finally up 2 m.

Read the question, now read it again.

Read carefully. Can I write the instructions as a number sentence?

Decide your operations and units.

I'll do 12 – 28 + 24 –13 + 7 – 6 + 2.

Approximate your answer.

If I add up all the positive numbers, they come to about 45.
If I add up all the negative numbers they come to about 50, so I think he'll end up around –5.

Calculate.

12 – 28 + 24 –13 + 7 – 6 + 2 = –2 m

Check.

I can check by adding all the positive numbers and subtracting all the negative numbers in a different order. Yes, I was correct!

Hints and tips

It can sometimes help to use a number line to count up or down. It is also useful to compare the answers to these two subtractions when the numbers are switched round: $28 - 12 = 16$, but $12 - 28 = -16$. When the first number is larger, the answer is positive. When the first number is smaller, the answer is negative.

Questions

1 a) Sam, the bungee jumper, starts at 18 m. He goes down 20 m, then up 15 m, then down 10 m and up 4 m. Where does he end up?

b) Seema starts at 20 m. She goes down 40 m, then up 25 m then down 16 m, and up 10 m. Where does she end up?

2 a) Zoe starts at 14 m. She goes down 28 m, then up 23 m then down 17 m, then up 10 m, then down 8 m and up 3 m. Where does she end up?

b) Clive, the bungee master, starts at 50 m. He goes down 85 m, up 32 m, down 28 m, up 16 m, down 11 m, up 9 m, down 4 m and finally up 1 m. Where does he end up?

CHALLENGE

Write three problems of your own, like this, for a partner to solve. Remember to work out the answers too!

Explore

Do this experiment to test for 'stretchiness'. Collect together a range of different pieces of string, rope, ribbon and elastic and a ruler. Cut them so that they are all the same length, for example 10 cm. Now stretch each piece to its maximum length and measure it and compare all the results and put them in order.

Measures

When solving problems about measures you need to be careful to use the correct units. For these questions you may use a calculator to help you work out the answers.

Here is the nutritional information from a can of baked beans.
(GDA stands for Guidance for Daily Amounts for adults.)

Typical values	Per 100g	Per $\frac{1}{2}$ can	GDA
Energy	73 calories	151 calories	2000 calories
Protein	4.9 g	10.0 g	45 g
Carbohydrate	12.9 g	26.7 g	230 g
(of which are sugars)	(5.0 g)	(10.4 g)	90 g
Fat	0.2 g	0.4 g	70 g
Fibre	3.8 g	7.9 g	24 g
Sodium	0.3 g	0.7 g	2.4 g
Salt equivalent	0.8 g	1.7 g	6 g

Mr Farrell eats a whole can of baked beans. How much fibre does the can contain and what approximate fraction of Mr Farrell's GDA of fibre is it?

Read the question, now read it again.

Read the table carefully. Think about what you are being asked.

Decide your operations and units.

I'll see how many grams of fibre are in a $\frac{1}{2}$ can and I'll double it. Then I'll see approximately what fraction of 24 g this is.

Approximate your answer.

7.9 g is about 8 g and 2 × 8 g = 16 g.

Calculate.

7.9 g × 2 = 15.8 g;
$\frac{16}{24} = \frac{4}{6} = \frac{2}{3}$;
It is about $\frac{2}{3}$ of his GDA.

Check.

I'll reread the question to make sure I have answered all of it.

Hints and tips

When calculating with decimals, be careful to put the decimal point of the answer in the right place. For example, 0.3 g x 7 = 2.1 g and 0.7 g + 0.3 = 1.0 g or 1 g, and so on.

Questions

1 a) Look at the table opposite. Susan eats 400 g of baked beans. How many grams of sugar does she eat?

b) Mrs Patel eats $\frac{1}{2}$ can of baked beans. Approximately what fraction of her GDA of protein is this? Give the fraction in its simplest form.

c) James eats 300 g of baked beans. How many grams of sodium does he eat?

2 a) Sam eats some baked beans. He has one quarter of his GDA of sodium in this portion. How many grams of baked beans does he eat?

b) Mr Brookman eats 200 g of baked beans. How many grams of salt equivalent does it contain and what approximate fraction of Mr Farrell's GDA of salt equivalent is this?

CHALLENGE!

Find the nutritional information for other food items in your cupboards. Write some problems of your own for a partner to answer about the information. Work out the answers so you can check your partner's calculations.

Explore

Do some research about healthy eating. Make a poster to help people choose the best foods to eat for their health. Give some nutritional information on your poster and include tips on how to cut down on the least healthy foods.

Area and perimeter

Perimeter is the distance around the edge of a shape (usually measured in cm). Area is the amount of surface inside it (usually measured in cm^2). When solving problems, don't mix the two up!

Fiona is printing some photos of different sizes.
Here are the lengths and widths of the photos she prints out.

	Photo A	Photo B	Photo C	Photo D
Length	15.0 cm	18.0 cm	25.4 cm	51.0 cm
Width	10.0 cm	12.7 cm	20.3 cm	30.5 cm

One of the photos has a perimeter of 163 cm.
What is the area of this photo?

Read the question, now read it again.

First I must find which photo has a perimeter of 163 cm.

Decide your operations and units.

Half of the perimeter is the length plus the width, so I'll halve 163 cm and then see which measurements add to 163. Then, I'll multiply the length by the width to find the area.

Approximate your answer.

Because the perimeter is so large, I think it'll be photo D, which will have an approximate area of $50 \times 30 = 1500\text{ cm}^2$.

Calculate.

$163\text{ cm} \div 2 = 81\text{ cm}$, so it is photo D ($51\text{ cm} + 30.5\text{ cm}$).
The area is $51\text{ cm} \times 30.5\text{ cm}$
$= 50 \times 30.5 + 1 \times 30.5$
$= 5 \times 305 + 30.5 = 1555.5\text{ cm}$.

Check.

I'll use a calculator to divide 1555.5 by 30.5 to check it's 51. It is!

Hints and tips

Areas can be found by counting whole squares inside a shape or by using a particular formula. The formula for finding the area (A) of a rectangle is $A = l \times w$ where l is the length and w, is the width. You may use a calculator for these questions.

Questions

1

a) Look at the table opposite. What is the perimeter of photo B?

b) What is the area of photo A? (Remember to give the correct unit.)

c) Which photo has a perimeter of 91.4 cm? How much more is this than the perimeter of photo A?

2

a) How much larger is the area of photo B than the area of photo A?

b) One of the photos has an area that is 515.62 cm^2. What is the perimeter of this photo?

c) What is the area of the four photos altogether?

CHALLENGE!

A small thumbnail photo is 6 cm × 4 cm. It is enlarged, so that the length of its sides are twice as long. Find the area of the thumbnail photo and of the enlarged photo. What do you notice about the areas?

4 cm

6 cm

Explore

Photos are still sometimes measured in inches, for example, 7 inches by 5 inches. How long is an inch in centimetres? Find out the relationship between centimetres and inches and write some equivalent lengths using both units. You could go to http://manuelsweb.com/in_cm.htm to find a converter.

Reading scales

When solving some word problems you may need to read a scale and then add, subtract, multiply or divide.

This scale shows the mass of two oranges.

About how many oranges would you get in a 1.5 kg bag?

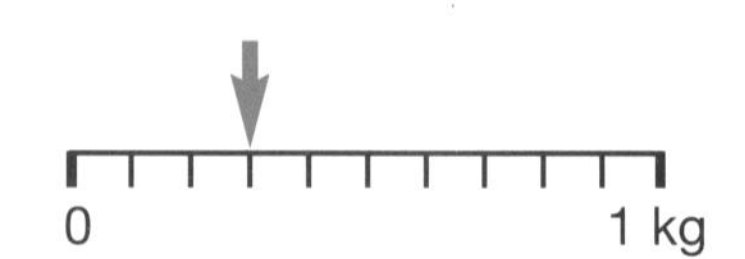

Read the question, now read it again.

Look carefully at the scale and work out what each interval is worth.

Decide your operations and units.

I need to read the scale and halve the result. Then I'll divide 1.5 kg or 1500 g by the answer. I may need to round.

Approximate your answer.

Each interval is worth 0.1 kg or 100 g, so the arrow is pointing to 300 g. Each orange weighs 150 g.

Calculate.

1500 g ÷ 150 g = 10, so the answer is 10 oranges.

Check.

I can multiply 150 g by 10 to check that I get 1.5 kg.

Hints and tips

To find the value of each interval on a scale, count how many spaces there are between numbered marks. Divide the difference between the numbers marked by the number of spaces. For example, on the scale above, between 0 and 1000 g (1 kg) there are 10 spaces. The difference between 0 and 1000 g is 1000 g, so divide 1000 g by 10 to get 100 g. Each interval is worth 100 g.

Questions

1 a) These two scales show the mass of a grapefruit and of a melon.

Grapefruit

0 500 g 1 kg

Melon

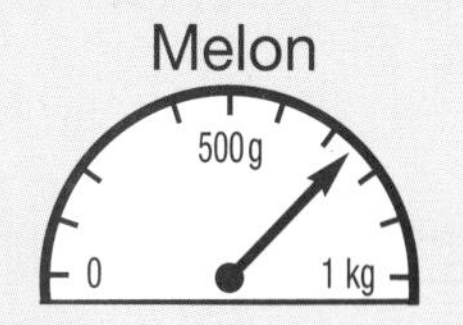

Jo puts three grapefruits and a melon into a plastic bag. What is the mass of the fruit altogether, in kilograms?

b) The mass of a watermelon is four times that of the grapefruit. What is the mass of the watermelon?

2 a) This scale shows the mass of one apple. About how many apples would you get in a 2 kg bag?

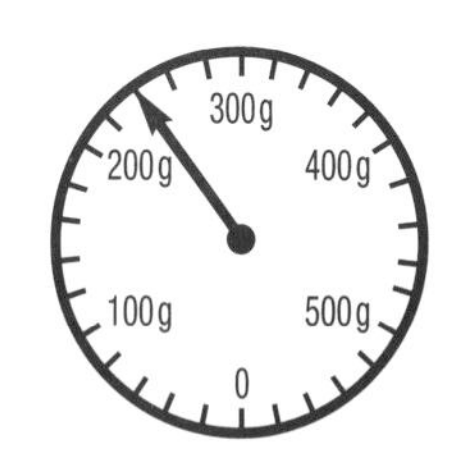

b) A banana weighs 75 g less than the apple shown in the scale above. Approximately how much will a bunch of six bananas this size weigh in kilograms?

c) This scale shows the mass of three avocados. About how many avocados would you get in a 2 kg bag?

0 1 kg

CHALLENGE!

A pepper weighs 150 g, a lettuce weighs 275 g and a bag of carrots weighs 400 g. Write some problems of your own about these items for a partner to solve. Remember to work out the answers too!

Explore

A lot of the fruit and vegetables that we buy come from other countries. Look at the labels of some fruit and vegetables and find out where they were grown. Find all the places on a world map and see how far they have been transported.

Time

For time problems you may need to add, subtract, multiply or divide time measurements to solve the problem and convert between units of time.

A kick-boxing session lasts 1 hour and 30 minutes. To earn a certificate, students have to attend sessions for 810 minutes. How many sessions is this?

Read the question, now read it again.	Read carefully. What do I need to do?
Decide your operations and units.	I must change 1 hour and 30 minutes to just minutes. I then need to divide 810 minutes by the answer.
Approximate your answer.	1 hour and 30 minutes is 60 + 30 = 90 minutes.
Calculate.	810 minutes ÷ 90 minutes = 9. So the answer is 9 sessions.
Check.	I can add 9 hours and $4\frac{1}{2}$ hours to get $13\frac{1}{2}$ hours, which is 13 × (60 + 30) = 810 minutes.

Hints and tips

Remember that there are 7 days in a week, 24 hours in a day, 60 minutes in an hour and 60 seconds in a minute.

Questions

1

a) An aerobics class lasts for 50 minutes. Urvi attends seven classes. How many hours and minutes is this in total?

b) A karate lesson is for 1 hour and 20 minutes. Dave attends six lessons. How many hours and minutes is this altogether?

c) A yoga session is 1 hour and 15 minutes. To earn a certificate, students have to attend sessions for ten hours. How many sessions is this?

2

a) Nick works out at the gym for 55 minutes a day, four days a week. How many weeks is it before he has worked out for 22 hours?

b) Sheena trains at the gym for 25 minutes a day, five days a week. How many hours and how many minutes will she train in seven weeks?

c) Angie runs a step-aerobics class for 50 minutes, followed immediately by a yoga class that is 1 hour 20 minutes long. She teaches these two classes every week for ten weeks. How many hours and minutes does she teach for, in total?

CHALLENGE

Julie works out at the gym for 35 minutes a day, five days a week and for 50 weeks a year. How many hours and minutes per year is this?

Explore

What are the benefits of keeping fit? Look online to find out five reasons why fitness is important. Find out what a sports person, e.g. David Beckham or Andy Murray, does to keep fit. How many hours do they spend working out? Write some notes about what you find out.

Angles

An angle is an amount of turn and is measured in degrees. When answering problems about angles always use the degree symbol (°) in your answers, e.g. 90°.

A triangle has an angle of 68° and an angle of 45°. What is the size of its third angle and it is acute or obtuse?

Read the question, now read it again.

Read slowly and carefully. What information have I been given?

Decide your operations and units.

The angles in any triangle have a total of 180° so I can add 68 and 45 together then subtract the answer from 180.

Approximate your answer.

70° + 40° = 110°; 180° – 110° = 70°
The answer will be about 70°.

Calculate.

68° + 45° = 113°
180° – 113° = 67°
The third angle is 67° and it is an acute angle.

Check.

I can check by adding 67°, 68° and 45° to see if the total is 180°. Yes, it is!

Hints and tips

Remember that the angles in any triangle add up to 180° and angles about a point add up to 360°. **Acute angles** are between 0° and 90° and **obtuse angles** are between 90° and 180°. **Isosceles triangles** have two sides and two angles of the same size.

Questions

1 a) A triangle has an angle of 88° and an angle of 25°. What is the size of its third angle and is it acute or obtuse?

b) Jim stands and faces north. He turns clockwise through 170° and then turns clockwise through 60°. Through what angle must he still turn clockwise to face north again?

c) A right-angled triangle has an angle of 55°. What is the size of the other two angles?

2 a) An isosceles triangle has two angles of 77°. What is the size of the third angle?

b) A triangle has an angle of 32° and an angle of 58°. What is the size of its third angle? What could you call this triangle?

c) An arrow on a circular dial of a washing machine is pointing up. It is turned clockwise through 66°. It then turns clockwise through an angle of 140° and finally is turned clockwise through 69°. How much further must it turn clockwise to point straight up again?

CHALLENGE

An isosceles triangle has an angle of 50°.
What could the other angles be?
There are two possible answers.

Explore

Pythagoras was a Greek mathematician who is famous for what he discovered about right-angled triangles. Look online and see if you can find out what he discovered and who he was. Write a newspaper report about what you find out.

Data handling

Data handling questions will ask you to look at a graph, chart or table and to use the data to answer the questions.

These pie charts show the proportion of players from different parts of the world for four football clubs. Each pie chart represents the 24 players in each squad.

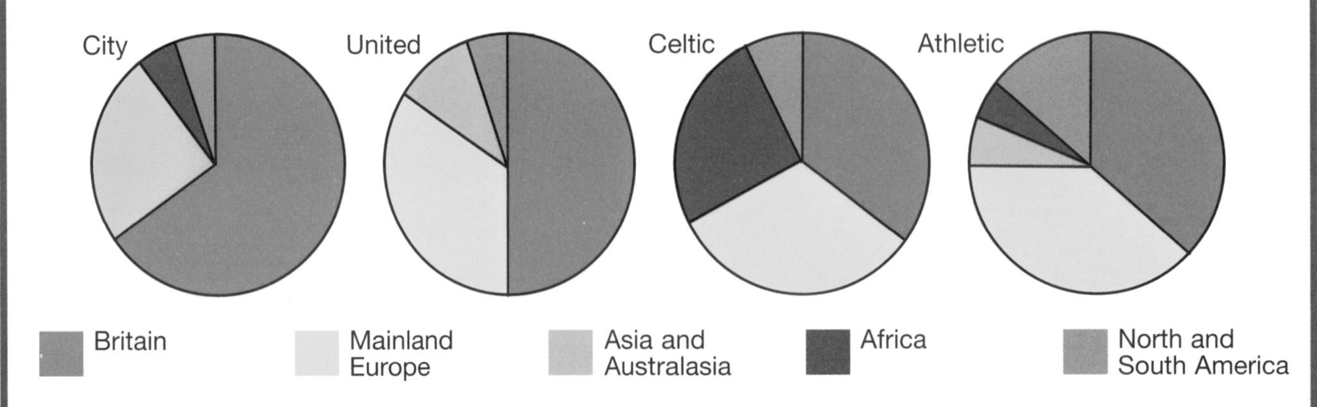

From the pie chart, what fraction of the United players are from mainland Europe and how many players is this?

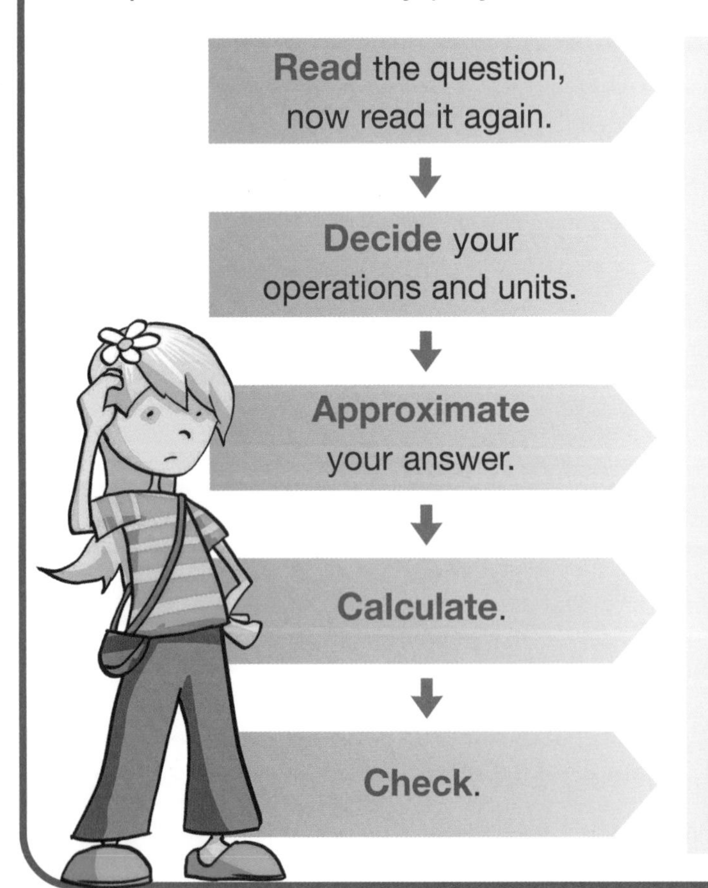

Read the question, now read it again.	Read slowly and carefully. Make sure you know what each pie represents.
Decide your operations and units.	I must estimate the fraction that is yellow for the second pie chart. Then I must find that fraction of the 24 players that represents.
Approximate your answer.	It looks about one third.
Calculate.	One third of 24 is 24 ÷ 3 = 8, so I think it is 8 players.
Check.	I can re-read the question to make sure I have answered it.

Hints and tips

Make sure you know what the whole of each pie represents. Here it is 24 players, so once you have estimated the fraction that is a particular colour you find that fraction of 24 to work out the number of players.

Questions

a) What fraction of the Celtic players are from Africa and how many players is this?

b) What fraction of the City players are from mainland Europe and how many players is this?

c) What fraction of the Athletic players are from Britain and mainland Europe and how many players is this?

2

a) What fraction of the Celtic players are from Britain and mainland Europe and how many players is this?

b) How many more players in the United squad are from Britain compared to the Athletic squad?

c) How many more players in the Celtic squad are from Africa compared to the City squad?

CHALLENGE!

Write your own problems about the data shown in the pie charts for a partner to solve. Make sure you work out the answers as well!

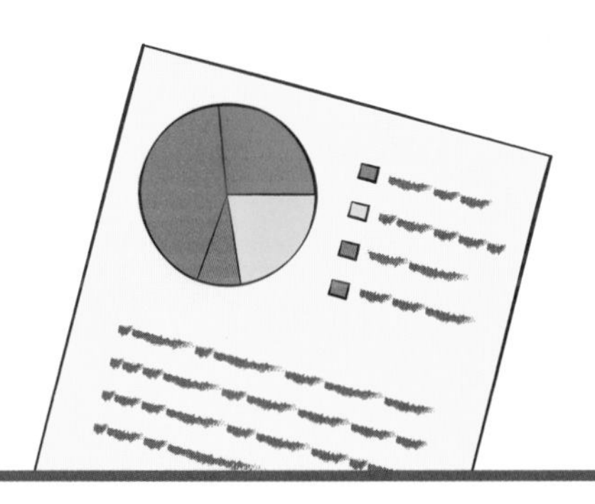

Explore

Find out about the nationalities of the players at your favourite football club. Go to their website and look for the information. Sketch a pie chart showing the approximate proportions from each area of the world.

Averages

An average is a typical value. There are three types of averages: the mean, the median and the mode. They all help us to describe a set of numbers more simply.

Katie is playing cards. She is holding these cards in her hand. What is the mean of the numbers on her cards (taking Ace to be 1)?

Read the question, now read it again.

Read slowly and carefully.
What am I being asked to do?

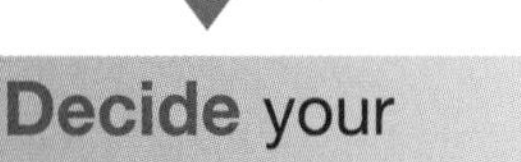

Decide your operations and units.

To find the mean I must add up all the numbers and then divide by the number of cards.

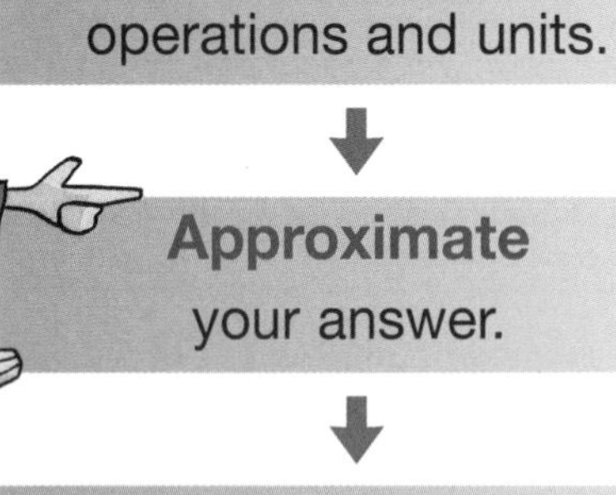

Approximate your answer.

The total looks about 30, so the mean will be about $30 \div 5 = 6$.

Calculate.

$10 + 7 + 7 + 5 + 1 = 30$; $30 \div 5 = 6$
So the mean is 6.

Check.

I can multiply my answer by 5 to make sure it gives 30. It does!

Hints and tips

To find the **mean**, you must work out the total of the numbers and then divide by the number of cards. The **mode** is the most common or frequently occurring number. To find the **median**, you must arrange the numbers in order first; the median is then the number in the middle.

Questions

1 a) Look at Katie's cards opposite. What is the mode and the median of the numbers?

Jaminda has these cards:

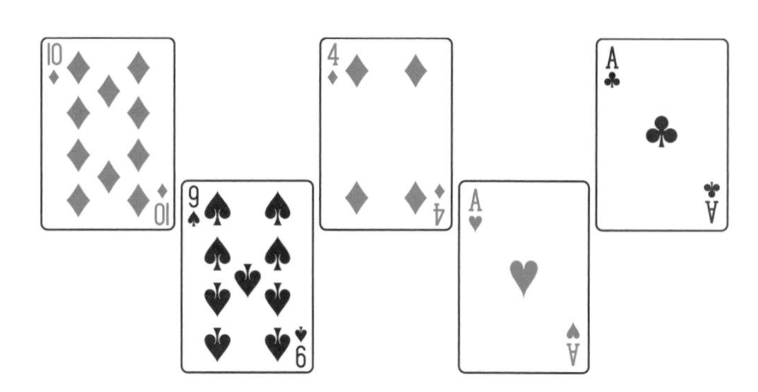

b) What is the mode?

c) What is the median?

d) What is the mean?

2 Liam has these cards:

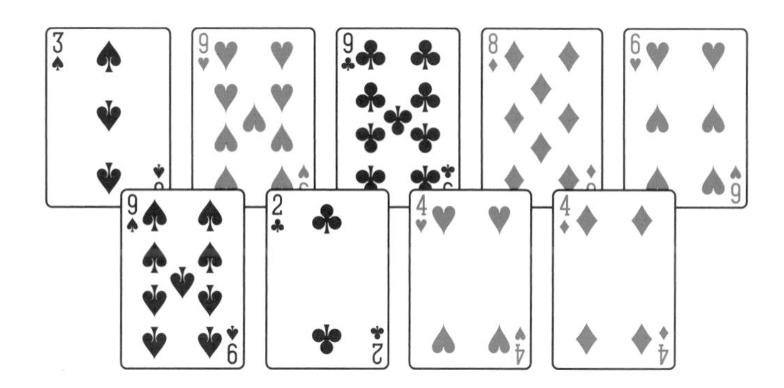

a) What is the mode?

b) What is the median?

c) What is the mean?

CHALLENGE!

The **range** of a set of numbers is the difference between the highest and lowest values. Jane has five cards, with a range of 7, a mean of 6, a mode of 5 and a median of 5. What could the numbers be?

Explore

Take a set of playing cards and remove the picture cards (Jacks, Queens and Kings). Deal yourself five cards and practise finding the mean, median, mode and range. Note that it is possible to have more than one mode.

Probability

Probability is the chance or likelihood that something will happen. When solving probability questions it is usual to give your answers as fractions.

Shahid is collecting picture cards of famous people from boxes of cereal. He has collected ten. Some of them are the same.

Without looking Shahid picks one of the ten cards. What is the probability that the person on the card is male? Give your answer as a fraction in its simplest form.

Read the question, now read it again.

Read slowly and carefully. What am I being asked to do?

Decide your operations and units.

I must see how many of the people are male, make a fraction over 10 and then simplify the fraction if I can.

Approximate your answer.

There seem to be more men than women so the probability will be larger than $\frac{1}{2}$.

Calculate.

I have counted 7 men so the probability is $\frac{7}{10}$. The fraction can't be simplified any more than this.

Check.

I can count up again to make sure I didn't miss any.

Hints and tips

Probability is how likely something is to happen. Where outcomes are **equally likely**, e.g. when rolling a dice, tossing a coin or picking cards, we can show the probabilities as a fraction, where the total number of possibilities is the denominator (bottom number) of the fraction. As there are 10 cards here and they are all equally likely to be picked, the denominator will be 10. If there is no chance the probability is zero.

Questions

Look at the cards opposite to answer all these questions.
Give all your answers as fractions in their simplest forms.

1 a) What is the probability that Shahid picks Marie Curie?

b) What is the probability that Shahid picks Isaac Newton?

2 a) What is the probability that he picks a person with the letter 'a' in their name?

b) What is the probability that he picks a person with the letter 'e' in their name?

CHALLENGE!

Shahid gets two more cards. One is of William Shakespeare and the other is of Vincent Van Gogh. He puts them with the other cards and picks one at random. What is the probability that the person he picks has three words in their name?

Explore

Choose one of the people from the cards and find out about their life. Write a short report for a history magazine about why they are famous. Include interesting dates such as when they were born, when they first became famous and so on.

Answers

Sequences
(Pages 10–11)
Questions:
1 a) 43, 91
b) 15, 1
c) 42, 33
2 a) 23.2, 46.8
b) 0, 5, 7.5

Mixed calculations (1)
(Pages 12–13)
Questions:
1 a) 3.09 cm
b) 97 g
c) 1.4 cm
2 a) Football
b) Volleyball
c) Cricket ball and hockey ball
Challenge:
143.52 g

Mixed calculations (2)
(Pages 14–15)
Questions:
1 a) 27 laps
b) Yes
2 a) £4.81
b) £9.75
Challenge:
Chloe raised the most (£10.50).

Fractions
(Pages 16–17)
Questions:
1 a) 3
b) 7
c) 20 angel fish
2 a) 10 frogs
b) 10 sheep
c) 4 bananas
Explore:
$\frac{3}{5} = \frac{1}{2} + \frac{1}{10}$ and $\frac{7}{8} = \frac{1}{2} + \frac{1}{4} + \frac{1}{8}$

Decimals
(Pages 18–19)
Questions:
1 a) 84 kg
b) 20.52 kg
c) 70 kg
2 a) 70 kg
b) 91.2 kg

Percentages
(Pages 20–21)
Questions:
1 a) £6650
b) 44
c) £200 000
2 a) 4044 women
b) £12 500
c) £187 500
Challenge:
£2750

Ratio and Proportion
(Pages 22–23)
Questions:
1 a) 80 g
b) 50 g
c) 60 g
2 a) 180 g courgettes, 75 g breadcrumbs
b) 45 g
c) 360 g courgettes, 240 g onions
Challenge:
1350 g

Simple formulae
(Pages 24–25)
Questions:
1 a) £23
b) £19
c) £22
2 a) 48 cm^2
b) 38 cm
c) 100 miles

Money and currencies
(Pages 26–27)
Questions:
1 a) £15
b) €30
c) £145.50
2 a) £8.23
b) £23.64
c) 5300 yen, cheaper by £4.30
Challenge:
60 000 yen is cheapest; cheaper by £5.56 than £455 and £6.85 less than $689.

Negative numbers
(Pages 28–29)
Questions:
1 a) 7 m
b) –1 m
2 a) –3 m
b) –20 m

Measures
(Pages 30–31)
Questions:
1 a) 20 g
b) Approx $\frac{1}{4}$
c) 0.9 g
2 a) 200 g
b) 1.6 g, approx $\frac{1}{4}$
c) 849 calories

Area and perimeter
(Pages 32–33)
Questions:
1 a) 61.4 cm
b) 150 cm^2
c) Photo C, 41.4 cm
2 a) 78.6 cm^2
b) 91.4 cm
c) 2449.72 cm^2
Challenge:
The area of the enlarged photo is four times the size of the thumbnail.

Reading scales
(Pages 34–35)
Questions:
1 a) 2.85 kg
b) 2.8 kg or 2800 g
2 a) about 8
b) 1 kg
c) 8

Time
(Pages 36–37)
Questions:
1 a) 5 hours 50 minutes
b) 8 hours
c) 8 sessions
2 a) 6 weeks
b) 14 hours 35 minutes
c) 21 hours 40 minutes
Challenge:
145 hours and 50 minutes

Angles
(Pages 38–39)
Questions:
1 a) 67°, acute
b) 130°
c) 90° and 35°
2 a) 26°
b) 90°; a right-angled triangle
c) 85°
Challenge:
50° and 80° or 65° and 65°

Data handling
(Pages 40–41)
Questions:
1 a) $\frac{1}{4}$, 6
b) $\frac{1}{4}$, 6
c) $\frac{3}{4}$, 18
2 a) $\frac{2}{3}$, 16
b) 4
c) 5

Averages
(Pages 42–43)
Questions:
1 a) Mode 7, median 7
b) 1
c) 4
d) 5
2 a) 9
b) 6
c) 6
Challenge:
Possible answer: 3, 5, 5, 7 and 10

Probability
(Pages 44–45)
Questions:
1 a) $\frac{1}{5}$
b) $\frac{3}{10}$
2 a) $\frac{9}{10}$
b) 1
Challenge:
$\frac{3}{12} = \frac{1}{4}$

Notes